INSPIRE MATHS

KU-246-394

PRACTICE BOOK 2B

Noogol

Googol

Koogol

Ooogol

Zoogol

Toogol

Rida

Consultant and author
Dr Fong Ho Kheong

Authors
Chelvi Ramakrishnan and Michelle Choo

UK consultants
Carole Skinner, Simon d'Angelo and Elizabeth Gibbs

Introduction

Inspire Maths is a comprehensive, activity-based programme designed to provide pupils with a firm foundation in maths and to develop the creative and critical thinking skills to become fluent problem solvers.

For the teacher:

Use **Practice** with well-structured questions to check and reinforce concepts learnt in the Pupil Textbook.

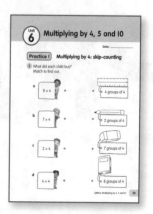

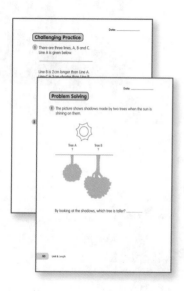

Develop pupils' creativity and critical thinking skills with **Challenging Practice** and **Problem Solving**.

Reviews after every two or three units consolidate the concepts learnt.

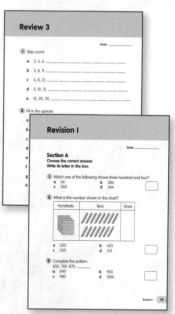

Revisions integrate topics, concepts and strands for complete consolidation.

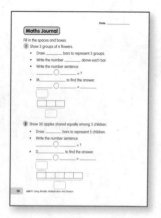

For the pupil:

Share what you have learnt, create your own questions and become aware of your own mathematical thinking in your **Maths Journal**.

Contents

Multiplying by 2 and 3

Date: _____

Multiplying by 2: skip-counting

1. Colour the shapes.
   Use the same colour for the shapes that give the same number.

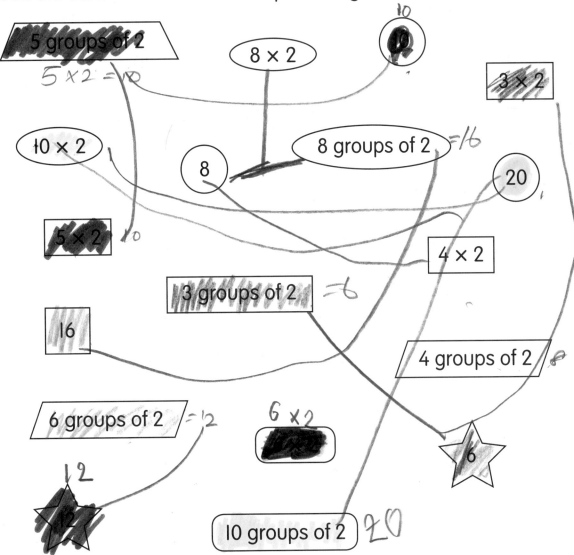

5 groups of 2   5 × 2 = 10

8 × 2

10

3 × 2

10 × 2

8

8 groups of 2   = 16

20

5 × 2   10

4 × 2

3 groups of 2   = 6

16

4 groups of 2

6 groups of 2   = 12

6 × 2

6

12

10 groups of 2   20

2 Count in twos.
Then fill in the spaces.

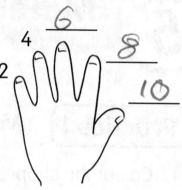

a   2, 4, _6_, _8_, 10

b   6, 8, 10, _12_, _14_, _____, 18

c   8, _10_, 12, 14, _16_, _18_, 20

d   _6_, _8_, 10, 12, 14, _16_, _18_

3 Fill in the spaces.

a   6 × 2 = _12_   b   3 × 2 = _6_

c   7 × 2 = _14_   d   4 × 2 = _8_

e   9 × 2 = _18_   f   5 × 2 = _10_

g   8 × 2 = _16_   h   1 × 2 = _2_

i   10 × 2 = _20_   j   2 × 2 = _4_

Practice 2 Multiplying by 2: using dot paper

Solve these word problems.

1 Peter has 4 bags.
He puts 2 buns into each bag.
How many buns does Peter have altogether?

4 × 2 = _8_

Peter has _8_ buns altogether.

2 6 children have 6 bicycles.
Each bicycle has 2 wheels.
How many wheels are there altogether?

_6_ × 2 = _12_

There are _12_ wheels altogether.

3 Mrs Smith buys 5 rolls for her children.
Each roll costs £2.
How much does Mrs Smith spend altogether?

_____5_____ × £2 = £ _____10_____

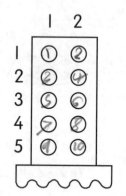

Mrs Smith spends £ ___10___ altogether.

4 Hardeep buys 9 balls.
Each ball costs £2.
How much do the balls cost altogether?

_____9_____ × £___2___ = £___18___

The balls cost £ ___18___ altogether.

5 Fill in the spaces.

a

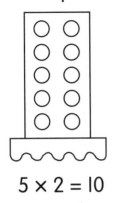

$5 \times 2 = 10$

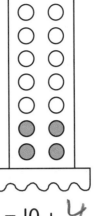

$7 \times 2 = 10 + \underline{4}$

$= \underline{14}$

b

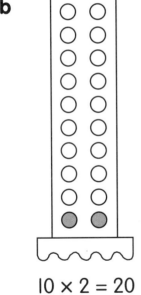

$10 \times 2 = 20$

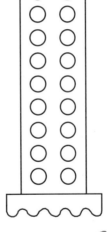

$9 \times 2 = 20 - \underline{2}$

$= \underline{18}$

c $6 \times 2 = 10 + \underline{12}$

$= \underline{12}$

d $8 \times 2 = 20 - \underline{4}$

$= \underline{16}$

6 Use the dot paper to help you answer these questions.

Example

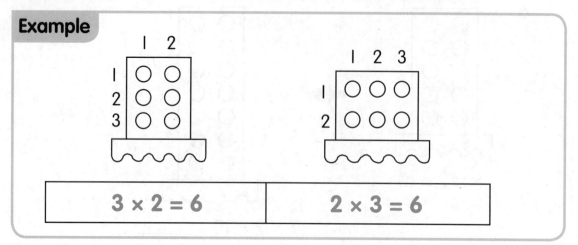

| $3 \times 2 = 6$ | $2 \times 3 = 6$ |

a

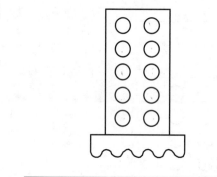

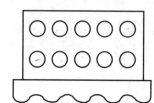

| $\underline{5} \times \underline{2} = \underline{10}$ | $2 \times \underline{5} = \underline{10}$ |

b

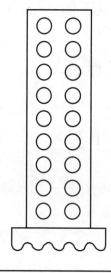

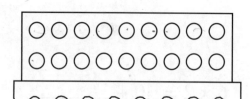

| $\underline{9} \times \underline{2} = \underline{18}$ | $\underline{2} \times \underline{9} = \underline{18}$ |

Practice 3   Multiplying by 3: skip-counting

1   Match the shapes with the same answers.

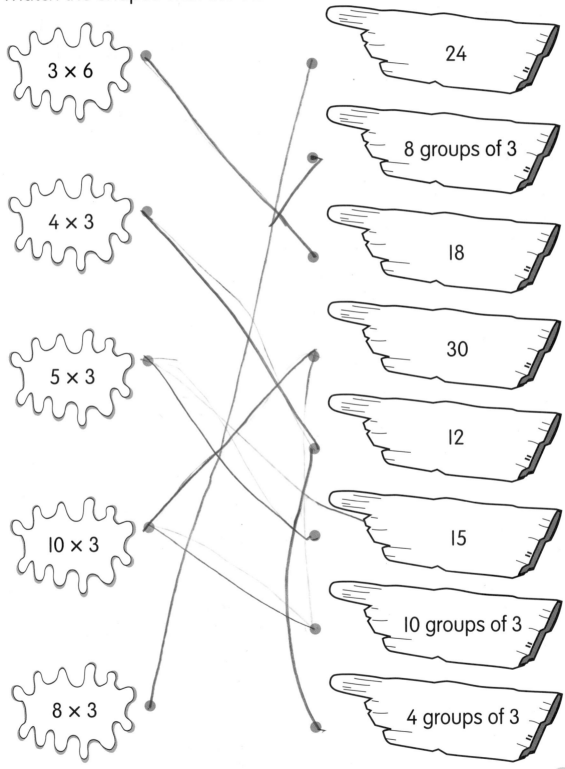

3×6

4×3

5×3

10×3

8×3

24

8 groups of 3

18

30

12

15

10 groups of 3

4 groups of 3

2 Count in threes.
Then fill in the spaces.

3, 6, 9, 12, _____, 18

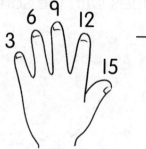
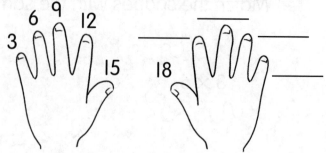

a   9, 12, 15, _____, _____, _____, _____

b   12, _____, 18, 21, _____, _____, 30

c   _____, _____, 15, 18, 21, _____, _____

3 Fill in the spaces.

a   4 × 3= _____

b   2 × 3 = _____

c   6 × 3= _____

d   8 × 3 = _____

e   9 × 3= _____

f   7 × 3 = _____

g   3 × 3= _____

h   10 × 3 = _____

Practice 4 Multiplying by 3: using dot paper

Solve these word problems.

1 Farha buys 4 kites.
Each kite costs £3.
How much does Farha pay for the kites?

4 × £3 = £ _____

Farha pays £ _____ for the kites.

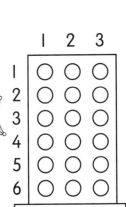

2 Jack buys 6 badges.
Each badge costs £3.
How much does he pay for all the badges?

_____ × £3 = £ _____

He pays £ _____ for all the badges.

3 Ruby sees 7 tricycles in a shop.
Each tricycle has 3 wheels.
How many wheels are there altogether?

_____ × _____ = _____

There are _____ wheels altogether.

4 Miss Brook divides a class of children into 8 groups.
There are 3 children in each group.
How many children are there in Miss Brook's class?

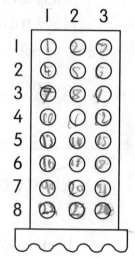

$\underline{3} \times \underline{8} = \underline{24}$

There are $\underline{24}$ children in Miss Brook's class.

5 Fill in the spaces.

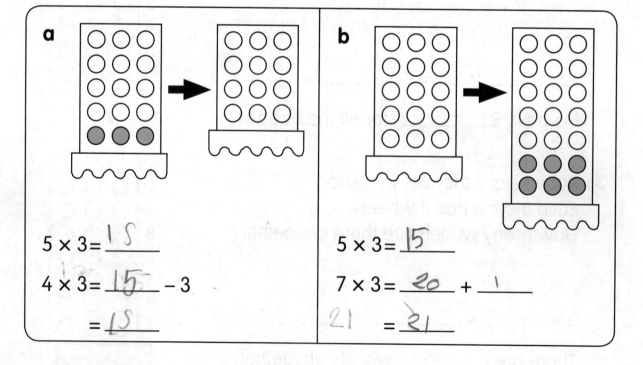

a

$5 \times 3 = \underline{15}$

$4 \times 3 = \underline{15} - 3$

$\quad = \underline{15}$

b

$5 \times 3 = \underline{15}$

$7 \times 3 = \underline{20} + \underline{1}$

$21 \quad = \underline{21}$

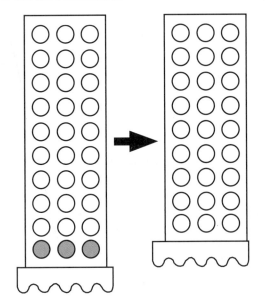

c

$10 \times 3 = \underline{30}$

$9 \times 3 = \underline{30} - \underline{3}$

$27 = \underline{27}$

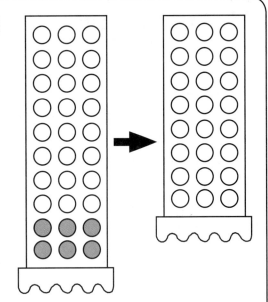

d

$10 \times 3 = \underline{30}$

$8 \times 3 = \underline{30} - \underline{8}$

$12 = \underline{12}$

6 Fill in the boxes.

Example

$\boxed{4} \times 3 = 12$

$3 \times \boxed{4} = 12$

```
      1   2   3
  1  ○   ○   ○
  2  ○   ○   ○
  3  ○   ○   ○
  4  ○   ○   ○
```

```
      1   2   3   4
  1  ○   ○   ○   ○
  2  ○   ○   ○   ○
  3  ○   ○   ○   ○
```

a $\boxed{6} \times 3 = 18$

$3 \times \boxed{6} = 18$

b $\boxed{7} \times 3 = 21$

$3 \times \boxed{7} = 21$

c $8 \times 3 = \boxed{24}$

$3 \times 8 = \boxed{24}$

d $\boxed{9} \times 3 = 27$

$3 \times \boxed{9} = 27$

Maths Journal

1 These items are sold in a supermarket.
Write a multiplication story in the space below.

soup — 1 for £1

marshmallows — 1 for £2

bread — 1 for £3

Story A

I buy 4 packets of marshmallows.

I pay ___£8___.

Story B

my mum told me to *buy* be
~~ofe~~ Soup. I *Paid* Paid £1. and 3
Bread Loafs I Pay £9.

Practice 5 Division

1 Fill in the spaces.
Then complete the division sentences.

$8 \div 2 =$ ___4___

I can count in twos.
2, 4, 6, 8
$4 \times 2 = 8$

a Count in twos.

2, _4_, _6_, _8_, _12_, _14_

$12 \div 2 =$ _6_

b Count in threes.

3, _6_, _9_, _12_, _15_, _18_, _21_, _24_

$24 \div 3 =$ _8_

2 Divide these numbers.

a $20 \div 2 =$ _10_   **b** $18 \div 3 =$ _6_

c $15 \div 3 =$ _5_   **d** $16 \div 2 =$ _8_

e $6 \div 2 =$ _3_   **f** $27 \div 3 =$ _9_

3 Mrs Khan gives 21 books to 3 children.
The 3 children share the books equally among themselves.
How many books does each child get?

$$\underline{21} \div \underline{3} = \underline{7}$$

Each child gets __7__ books.

4 Mr Thomas has 2 children.
He gives them £16 to share equally.
How much money does each child get?

$$£\underline{16} \div \underline{2} = £\underline{8}$$

Each child gets £ __8__.

5 Mrs Lee fries 27 eggs.
She shares them equally onto 3 plates.
How many fried eggs are there on each plate?

$$\underline{27} \div \underline{3} = \underline{9}$$

There are __9__ fried eggs on each plate.

6 Jack puts 12 pencils equally into 2 boxes.
How many pencils are there in each box?

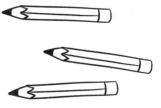

$$\underline{12} \div \underline{2} = \underline{6}$$

There are ___6___ pencils in each box.

7 Tai uses 9 straws to make 3 triangles of the same size.
How many straws are needed to make 1 triangle?

$$\underline{9} \div \underline{3} = \underline{3}$$

___3___ straws are needed to make 1 triangle.

8 Miya fixes 8 wheels on her toy cars.
She fixes 4 wheels on each car.
How many cars are there?

$$\underline{8} \div \underline{4} = \underline{2}$$

There are ___2___ cars.

9 Mr Williams cuts a melon into 18 pieces.
He puts 3 pieces into each bowl.
How many bowls does he use altogether?

$$\underline{18} \div \underline{3} = \underline{6}$$

He uses __6__ bowls altogether.

10 Omar fixes 20 wheels on his toy motorbikes.
He fixes 2 wheels on each motorbike.
How many toy motorbikes does Omar have?

$$\underline{20} \div \underline{2} = \underline{10}$$

Omar has __10__ toy motorbikes.

11 Abby has 9 fish.
She puts 3 fish in each fish tank.
How many fish tanks does she need?

$$\underline{9} \div \underline{3} = \underline{03}$$

She needs __3__ fish tanks.

Challenging Practice

1 Fill in the boxes with the correct numbers.

Date: _____

Problem Solving

1

I am a two-digit number.
I am more than 15 but less than 20.
I can be found in both the 2 and 3 times tables.
What number am I?

18

First write down the
2 and 3 times tables.

Unit 6 Multiplying by 4, 5 and 10

Date: _____

Practice 1   Multiplying by 4: skip-counting

1 What did each child buy?
Match to find out.

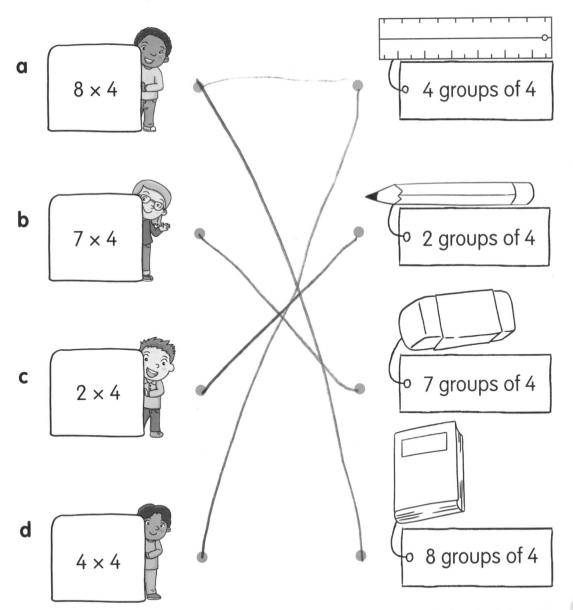

a 8 × 4

b 7 × 4

c 2 × 4

d 4 × 4

4 groups of 4

2 groups of 4

7 groups of 4

8 groups of 4

2 Count in fours.
Then fill in the spaces.

a   4, 8, 12, 16, __18__

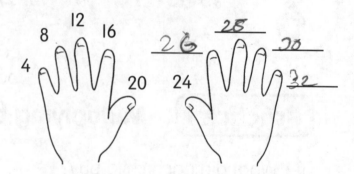

b   12, 16, 20, __22__, __24__, __26__, __28__

c   16, __18 20__, 24, 28, __30__, __32__, 40

d   __16__, __18__, 20, 24, 28, __30__, __32__

3 Fill in the spaces.

a $3 \times 4 = $ __12__   b $6 \times 4 = $ __24__

c $2 \times 4 = $ __8__   d $8 \times 4 = $ __32__

e $9 \times 4 = $ __36__   f $4 \times 4 = $ __16__

g $10 \times 4 = $ __40__   h $7 \times 4 = $ __22__

Date: _____

Practice 2   Multiplying by 4: using dot paper

1 Hardeep has 3 boxes.
He puts 4 coloured pencils in each box.
How many coloured pencils does Hardeep have altogether?

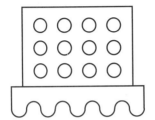

$3 \times 4 = \underline{12}$

Hardeep has _____12_____ coloured pencils altogether.

2 Ruby looks at the wheels of 6 toy cars.
Each car has 4 wheels.
How many wheels are there altogether?

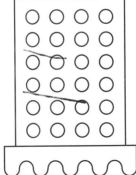

_____ $\times 4 = $ _____

There are _____ wheels altogether.

Unit 6: Multiplying by 4, 5 and 10   **25**

3 Mrs Jones buys 5 T-shirts for her children.
Each T-shirt costs £4.
How much does Mrs Jones spend altogether?

_5_ × £4 = £ _20_

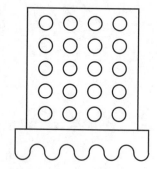

Mrs Jones spends £ _20_ altogether.

4 Mr Bell packs sandwiches for 8 children.
Each child gets 4 sandwiches.
How many sandwiches does Mr Bell pack?

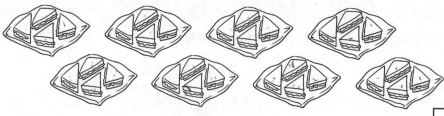

_8_ × _4_ = _32_

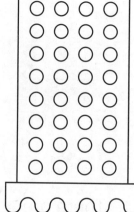

Mr Bell packs _32_ sandwiches.

5 Fill in the spaces.

a

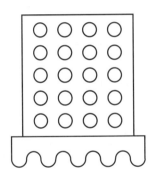

5 × 4 = _20_

6 × 4 = _20_ + 4

= _20_

b

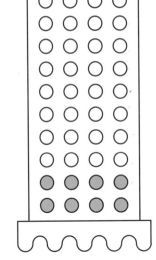

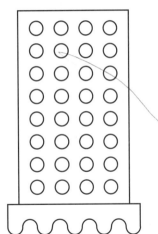

10 × 4 = _40_

8 × 4 = _24_ − 8

= _24_

c 7 × 4 = _20_ + 8

= _28_

d 9 × 4 = _____ − 4

= _____

6 Use the dot paper to help you find the answers.

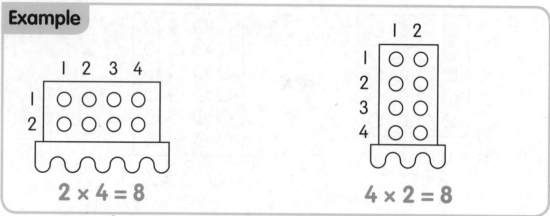

Example

$2 \times 4 = 8$

$4 \times 2 = 8$

a

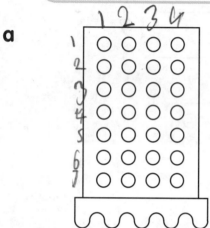

$\underline{7} \times \underline{4} = \underline{28}$

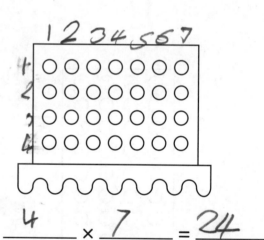

$\underline{4} \times \underline{7} = \underline{24}$

b

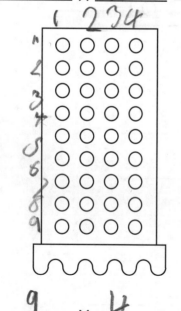

$\underline{9} \times \underline{4} = \underline{3\sqrt{}}$

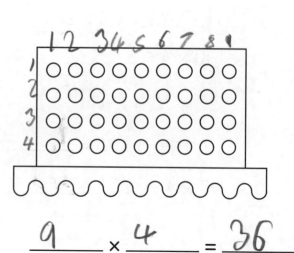

$\underline{9} \times \underline{4} = \underline{36}$

Practice 3 **Multiplying by 5: skip-counting**

1 Find the missing numbers.

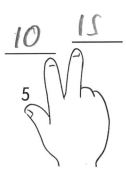

a 3 groups of 5 = _15_ × 5

= _15_

b 4 groups of 5 = _20_ × 5

= _20_

c 5 groups of 5 = _25_ × _5_

= _25_

d 7 groups of 5 = _35_ × _5_

= _35_

Use your fingers.

e 8 groups of 5 = _40_ × _5_

= _40_

f 9 groups of 5 = _45_ × _5_

= _45_

2 Count in fives.
Then fill in the spaces.

a   5, 10, 15, 20, 25, ___30___

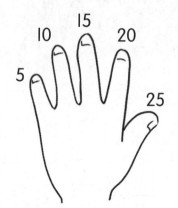 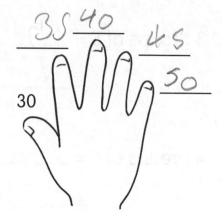

b   15, 20, 25, __30__ , __35__ , __40__ , __45__

c   20, __25__ , 30, __35__ , 40, 45

d   __15__ , __20__ , 25, 30, 35, __40__ , __45__ , __50__

3 Fill in the spaces.

a $3 \times 5 =$ __15__   b $2 \times 5 =$ __10__

c $6 \times 5 =$ __30__   d $8 \times 5 =$ __40__

e $9 \times 5 =$ __45__   f $7 \times 5 =$ __35__

g $5 \times 5 =$ __25__   h $10 \times 5 =$ __50__

4 Miss Evans asks three children to raise both their hands.
There are 5 fingers on each hand.
How many fingers do the three children have altogether?

$6 \times 5 = $ _30_

The three children have _30_ fingers altogether.

5 Mr Green buys 7 bowls of soup for his friends.
Each bowl of soup costs £5.
How much does Mr Green pay for the 7 bowls of soup?

£5

_7_ × £ _5_ = £ _35_

He pays £ _35_ for the 7 bowls of soup.

6 Tai has 9 trays.
He puts 5 mugs on each tray.
How many mugs does he have altogether?

_9_ × _5_ = _45_

He has _45_ mugs altogether.

Maths Journal

1 £5   a bag of cakes

£2   a bag of carrots

£1

a bag of tomatoes

£3   a box of cereal

Look at the pictures.
Write one multiplication story in the space below.
(Use the 4 and 5 times tables.)

Story A

I bag of carrots cost £2.

Mr Lee bought 4 bags of carrots.

How much did Mr Lee have to pay? *8*

Story B

I bag of cakes cost £5.

Mr Ree bought 6 bags of cakes.

and I 9Paged £30.

Practice 4   **Multiplying by 5: using dot paper**

1   Mr Ali buys some beads to make necklaces.
    He uses 5 beads to make one necklace.
    How many beads does he use to make
    8 necklaces?

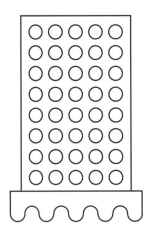

$\underline{\quad 5 \quad} \times \underline{\quad 8 \quad} = \underline{\quad 40 \quad}$

He uses $\underline{\quad 40 \quad}$ beads to make 8 necklaces.

2   9 children save up their pocket money.
    Each child saves £5.
    How much money do they save altogether?

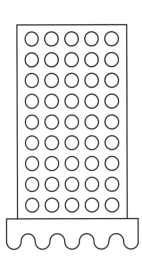

$\underline{\quad 5 \quad} \times £ \underline{\quad 9 \quad} = £ \underline{\quad 45 \quad}$

They save £ $\underline{\quad 45 \quad}$ altogether.

3   Ella packs some books equally into 10 boxes.
    She packs 5 books into each box.
    How many books does she pack altogether?

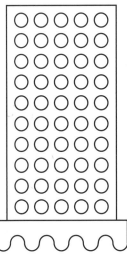

$\underline{\quad 5 \quad} \times \underline{\quad 10 \quad} = \underline{\quad 50 \quad}$

She packs $\underline{\quad 50 \quad}$ books into 10 boxes.

4 Use the dot paper.
   Colour the dots to help you find the answers.

a 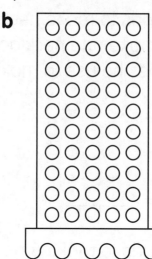   **b**   **c**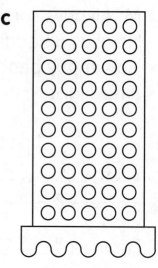

   $5 \times 5 =$ _____ $7 \times 5 =$ _____ $3 \times 5 =$ _____

5 Fill in the spaces.

a

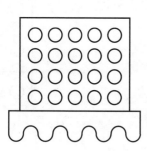   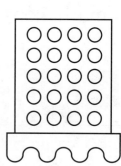

_____ $\times$ _____ = _____   _____ $\times$ _____ = _____

b

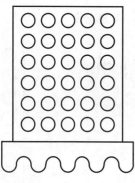   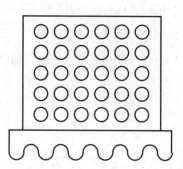

_____ $\times$ _____ = _____   _____ $\times$ _____ = _____

Practice 5 — Multiplying by 10: skip-counting and using dot paper

1 Fill in the spaces.

Example

$4 \times 1 = \underline{\quad 4 \quad}$

$4 \times 10 = \underline{\quad 40 \quad}$

a $7 \times 1 = \underline{\qquad}$

$7 \times 10 = \underline{\qquad}$

b $5 \times 1 = \underline{\qquad}$

$5 \times 10 = \underline{\qquad}$

c $3 \times 1 = \underline{\qquad}$

$3 \times 10 = \underline{\qquad}$

d $2 \times 1 = \underline{\qquad}$

$2 \times 10 = \underline{\qquad}$

e $8 \times 1 = \underline{\qquad}$

$8 \times 10 = \underline{\qquad}$

f $6 \times 1 = \underline{\qquad}$

$6 \times 10 = \underline{\qquad}$

2 Omar buys 4 sheets of stickers.
Each sheet has 10 stickers.
How many stickers does Omar have altogether?

$4 \times 10 = \underline{\qquad}$

Omar has _____ stickers altogether.

3 Farha makes 6 towers with some blocks.
She uses 10 blocks to make each tower.
How many blocks are needed to make the 6 towers?

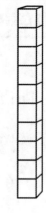

_____6_____ × 10 = _____60_____

_____60_____ blocks are needed to make the 6 towers.

4 Jack puts 10 cups on each tray.
How many cups are there on 8 trays?

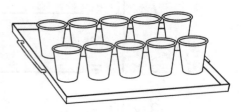

_____8_____ × 10 = _____80_____

There are _____80_____ cups on 8 trays.

5 There are 7 pea pods.
Each pea pod has 10 peas inside it.
How many peas are there in the 7 pea pods?

_____7_____ × _____10_____ = _____70_____

There are _____70_____ peas in the 7 pea pods.

6 Use the dot paper to help you find the answers.

a

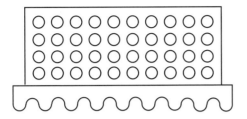

$4 \times 10 = \underline{40}$

$10 \times 4 = \underline{40}$

b

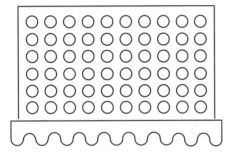

$\underline{10} \times \underline{10} = \underline{100}$

$\underline{9} \times \underline{10} = \underline{90}$

c

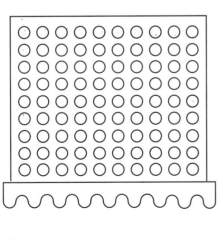

$\underline{10} \times \underline{10} = \underline{100}$

$\underline{10} \times \underline{9} = \underline{90}$

Maths Journal

1

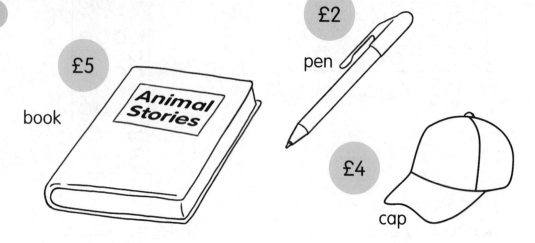

£5
book

£2
pen

£4
cap

Look at the pictures.
Write one multiplication story in the space below.
(Use the 5 and 10 times tables.)

Story A

Ruby bought 10 pens.

She paid £2 for each pen.

How much did she pay altogether?

£20

Story B

dsee bought 4 Book.
it cost £5 for each book.
and I Paid altogether £20

Practice 6   Division

1 Complete the multiplication sentences.
Then complete the division sentences.

$20 \div 5 =$ _100_

$4 \times 5 = 20$
$5 \times 4 = 20$

a $4 \times$ _4_ $= 16$

_4_ $\times 4 = 16$

$16 \div 4 =$ _4_

b $5 \times$ _5_ $= 25$

_5_ $\times 5 = 25$

$25 \div 5 =$ _5_

c $4 \times$ _6_ $= 24$

_6_ $\times 4 = 24$

$24 \div 4 =$ _4_

d $5 \times$ _3_ $= 15$

_3_ $\times 5 = 15$

$15 \div 5 =$ _3_

e $10 \times$ _9_ $= 90$

_9_ $\times 10 = 90$

$90 \div 10 =$ _oop_

f $4 \times$ _7_ $= 28$

_7_ $\times 4 = 28$

$28 \div 4 =$ _4_

g $10 \times$ _6_ $= 60$

_6_ $\times 10 = 60$

$60 \div 10 =$ _10_

h $5 \times$ _7_ $= 35$

_7_ $\times 5 = 35$

$35 \div 5 =$ _5_

2 Mr Cooper divides 30 beads equally among 5 children.
How many beads does each child get?

$$\underline{30} \div \underline{5} = \underline{5}$$

Each child gets ___5___ beads.

3 Peter uses 40 lolly sticks to make squares of the same size.
He makes a total of 10 squares.
How many lolly sticks does he use to make 1 square?

$$\underline{40} \div \underline{10} = \underline{140}$$

He uses ___140___ lolly sticks to make 1 square.

4 Mrs Ali has £36.
She divides the money equally among her 4 grandchildren.
How much money will each grandchild get?

$$£ \underline{36} \div \underline{4} = £ \underline{9}$$

Each grandchild will get £ ___9___.

5 Mr Harris has 45 cubes.
He gives each child 5 cubes.
How many children does Mr Harris have?

$$\underline{45} \div \underline{5} = \underline{9}$$

Mr Harris has __9__ children.

6 There are 40 children in a class.
There are 10 children in a team.
How many teams can be made from all the children in the class?

$$\underline{40} \div \underline{10} = \underline{4}$$

__4__ teams can be made.

7 Hardeep makes some necklaces with 35 beads.
He uses 5 beads to make one necklace.
How many necklaces can he make with all the beads?

$$\underline{35} \div \underline{5} = \underline{7}$$

He can make __7__ necklaces with all the beads.

8 Look at each multiplication sentence.
Then write two division sentences.

Example

$3 \times 4 = 12$

$$\underline{\quad 12 \quad} \div \underline{\quad 3 \quad} = \underline{\quad 4 \quad}$$

$$\underline{\quad 12 \quad} \div \underline{\quad 4 \quad} = \underline{\quad 3 \quad}$$

a $5 \times 4 = 20$

$$\underline{\quad 20 \quad} \div \underline{\quad 4 \quad} = \underline{\quad 5 \quad}$$

$$\underline{\quad 20 \quad} \div \underline{\quad 5 \quad} = \underline{\quad 4 \quad}$$

b $3 \times 5 = 15$

$$\underline{\quad 15 \quad} \div \underline{\quad 3 \quad} = \underline{\quad 5 \quad}$$

$$\underline{\quad 15 \quad} \div \underline{\quad 5 \quad} = \underline{\quad 3 \quad}$$

c $7 \times 10 = 70$

$$\underline{\quad 70 \quad} \div \underline{\quad 7 \quad} = \underline{\quad 10 \quad}$$

$$\underline{\quad 70 \quad} \div \underline{\quad 10 \quad} = \underline{\quad 7 \quad}$$

d $7 \times 5 = 35$

$$\underline{\quad 35 \quad} \div \underline{\quad 7 \quad} = \underline{\quad 5 \quad}$$

$$\underline{\quad 35 \quad} \div \underline{\quad 5 \quad} = \underline{\quad 7 \quad}$$

Challenging Practice

1. Tai has a book.
   He starts reading from page 7.
   He reads the book for 4 days.
   Each day, he reads 3 pages of the book.
   Which page will Tai stop at on the 4th day?

   (Hint: Draw a diagram to help you.) 12

2. Miss Brook chose children to work in a group.
   100 children were given numbers 1 to 100.
   She picked the child with the number 3.
   She then skip-counted in tens to pick the other children.
   Write down the numbers of the other children who were chosen.

   4

Problem Solving

1 A shop sells oranges and apples in bags.

bag of
10 oranges
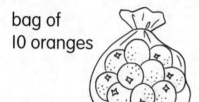

bag of
5 apples

For every 10 oranges Mr Williams buys, he also buys 5 apples.
He buys 20 oranges.
How many bags of fruit does he buy altogether?

(Hint: Draw a diagram to help you.)

10 + ro + 5 = 25

Review 3

1 Skip-count.

a 2, 4, 6, _8_, _10_, _12_, _14_, _16_, _16_, _20_

b 3, 6, 9, _12_, _15_, _18_, _21_, _24_, _27_, _30_

c 4, 8, 12, _16_, _20_, _24_, _28_, _32_, _36_, _40_

d 5, 10, 15, _20_, _25_, _30_, _35_, _40_, _40_, _50_

e 10, 20, 30, _40_, _50_, _60_, _70_, _80_, _90_, _100_

2 Fill in the spaces.

a 2 groups of 2 = _2_ × _2_ = _4_

b 5 groups of 2 = _5_ × _2_ = _10_

c 4 groups of 3 = _4_ × _3_ = _12_

d 8 groups of 3 = _37_ × _8_ = _24_

e 3 groups of 4 = _4_ × _5_ = _24_

f 9 groups of 4 = _4_ × _9_ = _36_

g 6 groups of 5 = _5_ × _6_ = _30_

h 7 groups of 5 = _5_ × _7_ = _35_

3 Complete the multiplication sentences.

a $4 \times 2 = 8$

   $2 \times 4 = 8$

b $7 \times 2 = 14$

   $2 \times 7 = 14$

c $7 \times 3 = 21$

   $3 \times 7 = 21$

d $6 \times 3 = 18$

   $3 \times 6 = 18$

e $5 \times 4 = 20$

   $4 \times 5 = 20$

f $8 \times 4 = 24$

   $4 \times 8 = 24$

g $3 \times 5 = 15$

   $5 \times 3 = 15$

h $9 \times 5 = 45$

   $5 \times 9 = 45$

i $4 \times 10 = 40$

   $10 \times 4 = 40$

j $6 \times 10 = 60$

   $10 \times 6 = 60$

4 Fill in the spaces.

a $6 \times 2 = 16$

b $9 \times 2 = 18$

c $9 \times 3 = 27$

d $6 \times 3 = 18$

e $3 \times 4 = 12$

f $6 \times 4 = 24$

g $8 \times 5 = 40$

h $5 \times 5 = 25$

i $7 \times 10 = 70$

j $5 \times 10 = 50$

5 Complete the multiplication and division sentences.

a	_6_ × 2 = 16	16 ÷ 2 = _8_	16 ÷ _7_ = 2
b	_4_ × 3 = 12	12 ÷ 3 = _4_	12 ÷ _4_ = 3
c	_7_ × 4 = 28	28 ÷ 4 = _7_	28 ÷ _7_ = 4
d	_6_ × 5 = 30	30 ÷ 5 = _6_	30 ÷ _6_ = 5
e	_2_ × 10 = 20	20 ÷ 10 = _2_	20 ÷ _2_ = 10

6 There are 3 plates.
Ella puts 3 pears on each plate.
How many pears are there altogether?

9

7 There are 18 balls.
Peter divides the balls into 2 equal groups.
How many balls are there in each group?

9

8 Miya spends £30 on some books.
Each book costs £10.
How many books does Miya buy?

3

9 Tai has 20 marbles.
He puts 4 marbles into each box.
How many boxes does Tai have?

5

10 Mrs Clark has 30 carrot sticks.
She gives them to some children.
　a　If each child gets 5 carrot sticks, how many children are there?
　b　If there are 10 children, how many carrot sticks will each child get?

7

Unit 7 — Using Models: Multiplication and Division

Practice I Multiplication

I Look at the models.
Then fill in the spaces.

a Ruby has 3 baskets of strawberries.
There are 5 strawberries in each basket.
How many strawberries does Ruby have altogether?

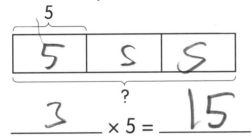

5

| 5 | 5 | 5 |

?

_3_ × 5 = _15_

Ruby has _15_ strawberries altogether.

_3_ groups
of 5 strawberries

b Jack has 4 boxes of toys.
There are 8 toys in each box.
How many toys does Jack have?

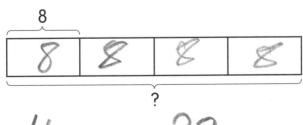

8

| 8 | 8 | 8 | 8 |

?

_4_ × 8 = _32_

Jack has _32_ toys.

_4_ groups
of 8 toys = 32

2 Complete the models.
Then fill in the spaces.

a Omar reads 10 pages of his book each day.
How many pages does Omar read in 3 days?

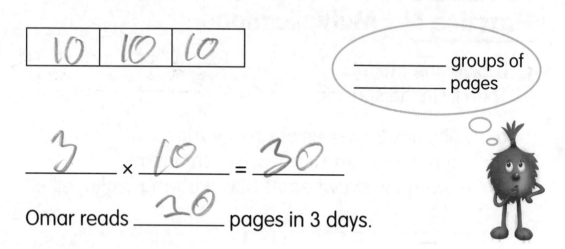

| 10 | 10 | 10 |

_____ groups of
_____ pages

$\underline{3} \times \underline{10} = \underline{30}$

Omar reads ___20___ pages in 3 days.

b There are 7 boxes.
There are 5 toys in each box.
How many toys are there in the 7 boxes?

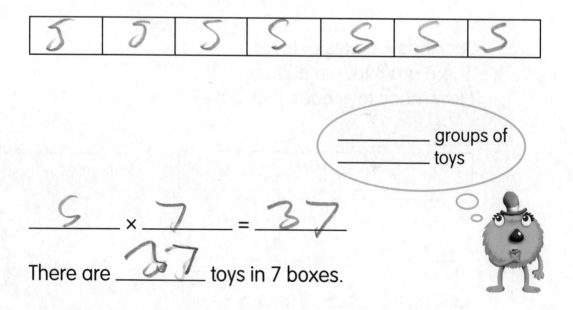

| 5 | 5 | 5 | 5 | 5 | 5 | 5 |

_____ groups of
_____ toys

$\underline{5} \times \underline{7} = \underline{37}$

There are ___37___ toys in 7 boxes.

3 Draw models to solve the word problems.

a There are 4 fish tanks.
There are 7 goldfish in each tank.
How many goldfish are there altogether?

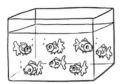 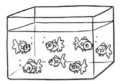 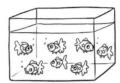 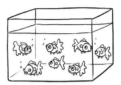

b Farha buys 5 packets of stickers.
There are 10 stickers in each packet.
How many stickers does Farha buy?

c   Jack has 3 boxes of chocolates.
There are 9 chocolates in each box.
How many chocolates are there altogether?

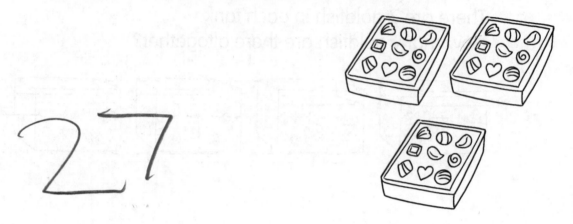

27

d   Millie fills 5 bags with marbles.
She puts 6 marbles in each bag.
How many marbles does Millie have altogether?

Practice 2 Division

1 Tick the box to show the correct model.

a Divide 15 children into 5 groups.
How many children will there be in each group?

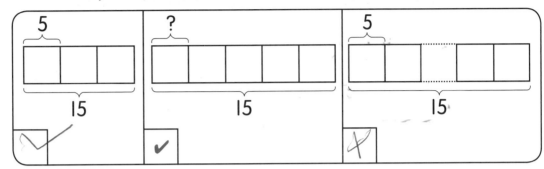

b Share 20 tomatoes equally on 4 plates.
How many tomatoes will there be on each plate?

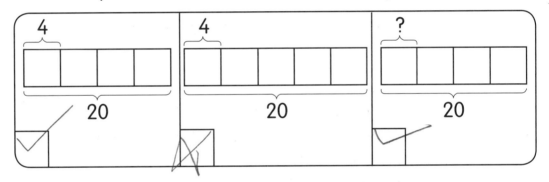

c Group 21 stickers equally to put onto some toy cars.
Put 3 stickers on each car.
How many toy cars are there?

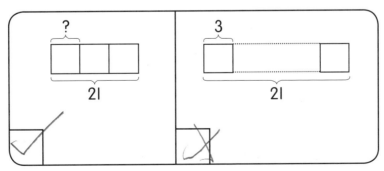

2 Look at the models.
Then fill in the boxes and spaces.

a Miss Green has 12 teddy bears.
She divides the teddy bears equally among 4 children.
How many teddy bears does each child get?

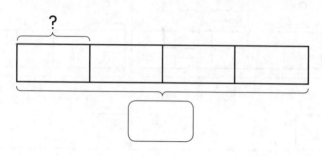

_____ ÷ _____ = _____

Each child gets _____ teddy bears.

b Hardeep has 36 seeds and 4 pots.
He plants an equal number of seeds in each pot.
How many seeds are there in each pot?

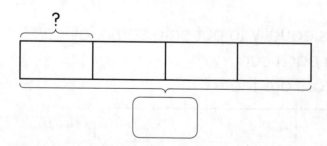

_____ ÷ _____ = _____

There are _____ seeds in each pot.

c Mrs Kelly buys 35 apples.
She gives the apples to some children.
Each child gets 5 apples.
How many children are there?

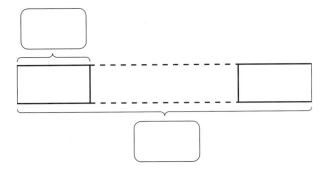

_____ ÷ _____ = _____

There are _____ children.

d Farha buys 24 presents for her friends.
Each friend gets 3 presents.
How many friends does Farha have?

_____ ÷ _____ = _____

Farha has _____ friends.

3 Draw models to solve the word problems.

a Mr Harris shares 40 cards equally among 4 children.
How many cards does each child get?

$$4 \times 10 = 40$$

b Tom writes 40 words in his writing book.
He writes 10 words on each page.
How many pages does Tom use?

$$? \ 10 \times = 40$$

4

Practice 3 | Multiplication and division

1 Tai has 5 cups.
He puts 10 straws in each cup.
How many straws does Tai use altogether?

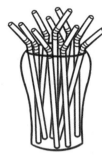

$?\ 10 = 50$
5

2 Ella reads 28 pages of a book.
She reads 4 pages each day.
How many days has Ella been reading?

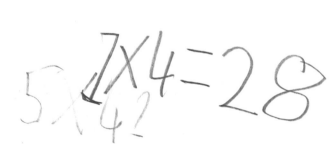

7

$5 \times 7 \times 4 = 28$

3 There are 3 tricycles in a shop.
Each tricycle has 3 wheels.
How many wheels do the tricycles have altogether?

9

$3 \times 3 = 9$

Maths Journal

Fill in the spaces and boxes.

1 Show 3 groups of 6 flowers.

- Draw ___6___ bars to represent 3 groups.
- Write the number ___3___ above each bar.
- Write the number sentence.

  ___6___ ⑦ ___3___ = ?

- M_el_____ to find the answer.

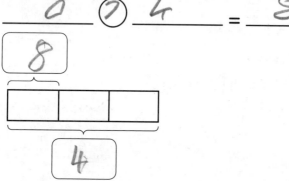

  ___8___ ⑦ ___4___ = ___8___

2 Show 30 apples shared equally among 5 children.

- Draw ___30___ bars to represent 5 children.
- Write the number sentence.

  ___30___ ⊙ ___5___ = ?

- D__Nang_____ to find the answer.

  ___30___ ⊙ ___5___ = ___6___

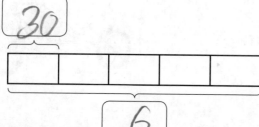

Date: _____

Practice 1   Measuring in metres

1   Look at the pictures.
    Fill in the spaces with **more** or **less**.

a

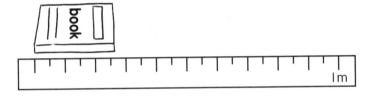

The length of the book is ___less___ than 1 m.

b

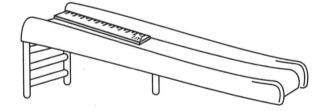

The length of the slide is _more_ than 1 m.

c

The height of the bookcase is
more than 1 m.

2 Look at the metre rulers in each picture.

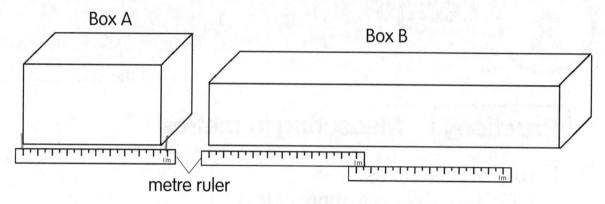

Box A

Box B

metre ruler

a Which box is about 1 m long? _A_

b Fill in the spaces with **more** or **less**.

Box A is _less_ than 1 m long.

Box B is _More_ than 2 m long.

3

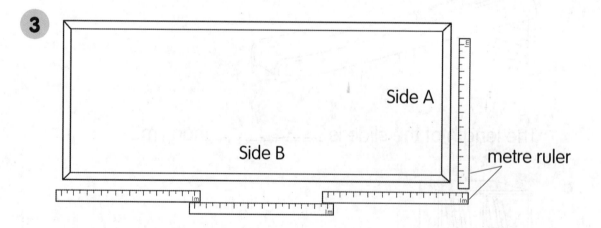

Side A

Side B

metre ruler

a Which side of the board is about 3 m long? _B_

b Side A is longer than _1_ m.

c Side B is shorter than _1_ m.

4 Look at the list below.
Tick (✔) the columns that are true for each object.
You will need a metre ruler or a piece of string 1 m long to
measure some of these objects.

Object	Less Than 1 m	More Than 1 m	More Than 1 m but Less Than 2 m	More Than 2 m
Door		✔		
Desk	✔			
Whiteboard	✔	✔		
Chair	✔			
Bin	✔			

5 Name three things that fit each of the lengths below.

Length	Things
Less than I m long	Book
About I m long	door
More than I m long	Cctbird

6 You will need 4 pieces of string of different lengths.
Make a guess about the length of each string.
Then use a metre ruler to find the actual length.

Things	My guess	Actual length
String A	about I m	I m
String B	Less 1m	50cms1
String C	More 1m	2 m
String D	Less 1m	100cm
string e	More 1m	3 m

Fill in the last row with anything you would like to measure.

Practice 2 Comparing lengths in metres

1 Look at the two ropes.

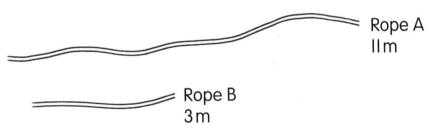

Rope A
11 m

Rope B
3 m

Which rope is longer? _A_____

How much longer is it? ___8 m____

2 Look at the 2 giraffes.

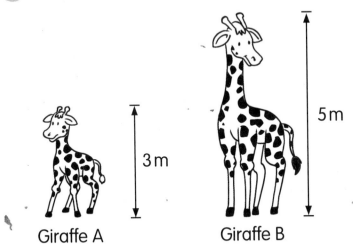

3 m

5 m

Giraffe A   Giraffe B

Which giraffe is taller? _B_____

How much taller is it? ___2 m____

3 Look at the lengths of the rectangle.

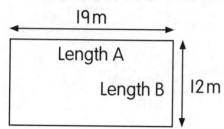

19m

Length A

Length B   12m

    a   Which is longer, Length A or Length B? __A__

    b   How much longer? __11__ m

4 Look at the buildings below.

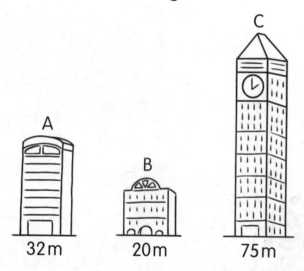

C

A

B

32m   20m   75m

    a   Which building is the tallest? Building __C__

    b   How much taller is Building C than Building A? __13__ m

    c   Building B is __13__ m shorter than Building C.

Practice 3 Measuring in centimetres

1 Use a ruler to draw these lines in the boxes.

Example

Line AB which is 5 cm long.

A————————B

a Line CD which is 12 cm long.

b Line EF which is 9 cm long.

c Line GH which is 6 cm long.

d Line MN which is 2 cm shorter than Line EF.

e Line XY which is 2 cm longer than Line GH.

2 Use a piece of string and a ruler to measure these lines and fill in the spaces.

a How long is the string? _100_ cm

string

b This string is used to make the following shapes. Use a piece of string and a ruler to measure them.

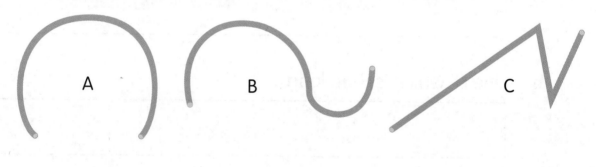

A

B

C

_50_ cm   _60_ cm   _70_ cm

Do they all have the same length? _no_

c What have you learnt?

wen   if   you   think
that   same   lengin but it is not.

Practice 4 | Comparing lengths in centimetres

1 Fill in the spaces.

a Which is longer? Line _both_

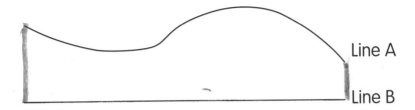

Line A

Line B

b Which is the longest?

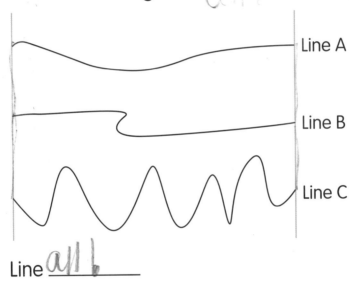

Line A

Line B

Line C

Line _all b_

2 Tick (✔) the correct way to measure the length of the pencil.

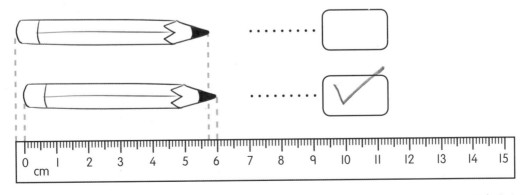

3 Find the length of each object below.

a

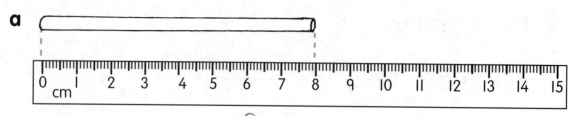

The straw is about ___8___ cm long.

b

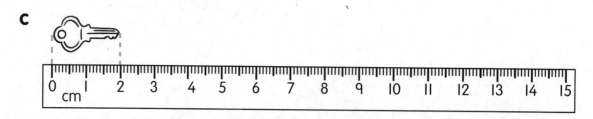

The wallet is about ___6___ cm long.

c

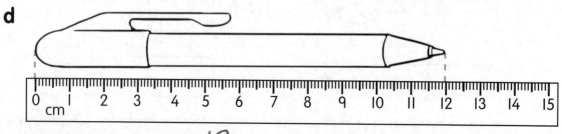

The key is about ___2___ cm long.

d

The pen is about ___12___ cm long.

e

The bracelet is about ___5___ cm wide.

For questions **f** to **h**, fill in the spaces with **longer** or **shorter**.

f   The pen is ___Longer___ than the straw.

g   The key is ___Shorter___ than the pen.

h   The wallet is ___Shorter___ than the straw.

i   The straw is ___6___ cm longer than the key.

j   The straw is ___4___ cm shorter than the pen.

k   The longest object is the ___Pet___.

l   The shortest object is the ___Key___.

4 Look at your fingers.
Use a ruler to help you measure your fingers.

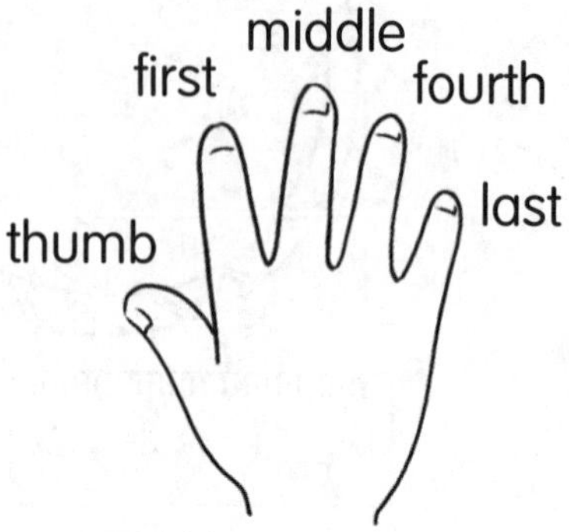

a Name your longest finger. _middle_

How long is it? __5__ cm

b Name your shortest finger. _last_

How long is it? __2__ cm

c How much longer is your middle finger than your thumb?
__1__ cm

(labels: first, middle, fourth, thumb, last)

5 Name three things that fit each of the lengths below.

Length	Things
Less than 1 cm long	bed
About 5 cm long	Stese
More than 5 cm long	hovese

Practice 5 **Addition and subtraction of length**

Find the answer to the joke below.

How do you count a herd of cows?

1 Add.

a $8m + 90m = \boxed{98}$ m $\cdots\cdots\cdots\cdots\cdots\cdots$ **C**

b $59cm + 142cm = \boxed{6|3}$ cm $\cdots\cdots\cdots\cdots$ **L**

c $231cm + 436cm = \boxed{667}$ cm $\cdots\cdots\cdots$ **U**

d $4m + 4m + 4m = \boxed{12}$ m $\cdots\cdots\cdots\cdots$ **A**

e $6m + 6m + 6m = \boxed{18}$ m $\cdots\cdots\cdots\cdots$ **W**

2 Subtract.

a 814 cm – 201 cm = $\boxed{603}$ cm . . . .   **R**

b 78 cm – 69 cm = $\boxed{11}$ cm . . . .   **S**

c 376 m – 216 m = $\boxed{160}$ m . . . .   **T**

d 96 m – 90 m = $\boxed{6}$ m . . . .   **E**

e 156 m – 79 m = $\boxed{653}$ m . . . .   **O**

Now match the letters to the numbers.

		E
667	9	6

12

98	77	18	98	667	201	12	160	77	613

3

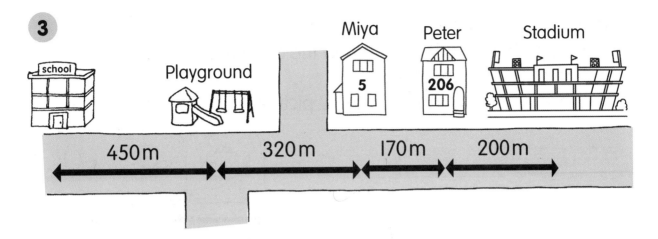

Miya lives in house number 5 and Peter lives in house number 206. Both of them go to the same school.

a How far is Peter's house from the playground? __320__ m

b How far is Miya's house from the playground? __170__ m

c Who lives nearer to the school, Miya or Peter? __Miya__

How much nearer? __250__ m

d If Miya goes to the stadium from her house, how far does she have to walk? __2__ m

e Peter and his mum walk from their house to the stadium.
They have walked 123 m.
How much further do they have to walk? __1__ m

4 Millie has 2 pictures.
One of them is 35 cm long and the other is 86 cm long.
She puts them together.
What is the total length of the 2 pictures?

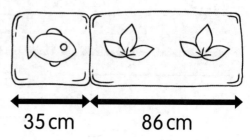

35 cm   86 cm

The total length is ___111___ cm.

5 Ella cuts a ribbon into 3 pieces.
The pieces are 4 m, 6 m and 2 m long.
How long was the ribbon before it was cut?

The ribbon was ___12___ m long.

6 Tai has 2 pairs of socks.
The red pair is 19 cm long.
The yellow pair is 22 cm long.
a   Which pair of socks is longer?
b   How much longer?

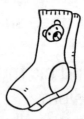

a   The ___yellow___ pair of socks is longer.

b   It is ___22___ cm longer.

7 A flag pole is 450 cm tall.
The flag is 345 cm from the ground.
How much further does it need to be raised to reach
the top?

8 The total length of two pieces of wood is 215 cm.
The first piece is 135 cm long.
   a   What is the length of the second piece?
   b   How much shorter is the second piece than the first piece?

   a   The length of the second piece is ___4___ cm.

   b   The second piece is ___4___ cm shorter than the first piece.

9 Tom is 135 cm tall.
He is 18 cm taller than Amit.
Amit is shorter than Ben by 30 cm.
How tall is Ben?

10 Peter cuts a strip of paper 10 cm long into three pieces.
One piece is 4 cm long.
The second piece is 3 cm long.
How long is the third piece of paper?

The third piece of paper is __12__ cm long.

11 Omar runs once round the field shown below.
How far does he run?

8 m

5 m   13   5 m

8 m

12 Ruby has 200 cm of string.
She uses 63 cm of it to fix a kite.
She gives 48 cm of it to Hardeep.
How much string does she have left?

89 cms

$$\begin{array}{r} 2\,0\,0 \\ -\ 6\,3 \\ \hline 1\,3\,7 \\ -\ 4\,8 \\ \hline 8\,9 \end{array}$$

Practice 6   Multiplication and division of length

1 Millie exercises every day by walking along an 8 m long path.
She walks along the path 3 times every day.
How far does she walk every day?

24

2 Anna cuts 6 strips of paper each 5 cm long.
She sticks them all together to make one long strip.
How long is this strip of paper?

30 CM

3 Ella has a ribbon 21 cm long.
She cuts it into 3 equal pieces.
How long is each piece?

4 Farha has a 30 cm long string.
She cuts it into pieces of equal length.
Each piece is 5 cm long.
How many pieces does she cut?

6   5×6=(30)

5 A strip of paper, 40 cm long, is cut into 4 equal pieces.
How long is each piece?

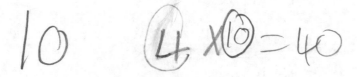

10   (4 × 10 = 40

6 Mr Williams makes some curtains.
He uses 5 m of fabric for each curtain.
How many curtains does he make with 45 m of fabric?

9   (9) × 5 = 45

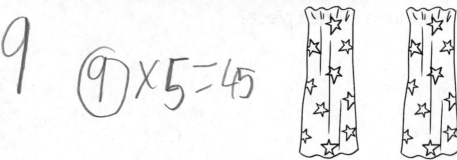

Date: _____

Challenging Practice

1 There are three lines, A, B and C.
Line A is given below.

_____

Line B is 2 cm longer than Line A.
Line C is 3 cm shorter than Line B.
How long is Line C?

_____

2 Mr Edwards uses some sticky tape to tape around the box as shown in the picture.
What is the shortest possible length of sticky tape that Mr Edwards uses?

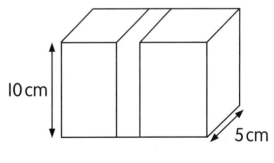

10 cm

5 cm

5 CM

Problem Solving

1 The picture shows shadows made by two trees when the sun is shining on them.

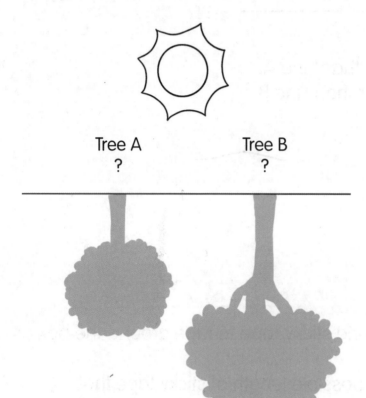

Tree A
?

Tree B
?

By looking at the shadows, which tree is taller?

Unit 9 Mass

Date: _____

Practice 1 **Measuring in kilograms**

1 Fill in the spaces with the words below.

more than	less than	as heavy as
parcel	cake	pear

a

The cake is _as heavy as_ 1 kg.

b

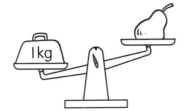

The mass of the pear is
less than 1 kg.

c

The mass of the parcel is
more than 1 kg.

d The _pear_ is the lightest.

e The _parcel_ is the heaviest.

2 Read the scales and fill in the masses.

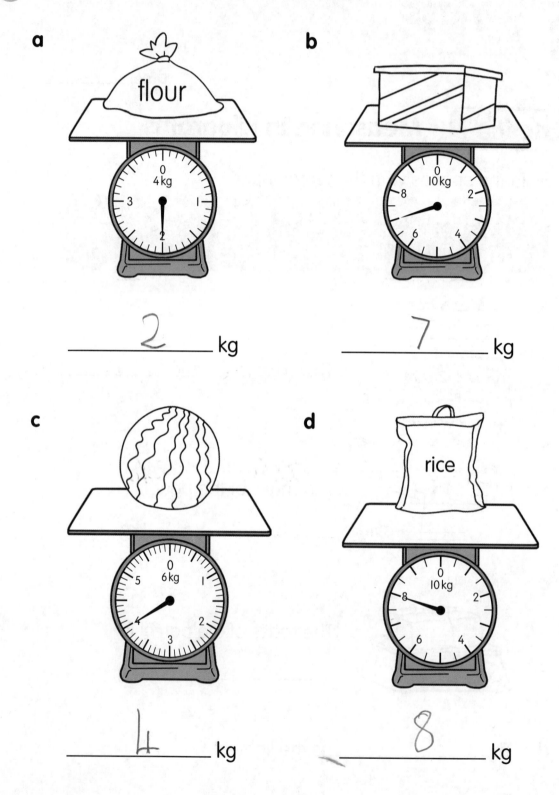

a

flour

_____2_____ kg

b

_____7_____ kg

c

_____4_____ kg

d

rice

_____8_____ kg

Practice 2 **Comparing masses in kilograms**

1

bag of oranges

bag of pears

a The mass of the bag of oranges is _____2_____ kg.

b The mass of the bag of pears is _____3_____ kg.

c Which bag is heavier? ___bag of pears___

How much heavier? _____1_____ kg

d The total mass of the bag of oranges and the bag of

pears is _____5_____ kg.

2 Mr Bell goes to the market.
He buys three bags of vegetables.

potatoes   carrots   onions

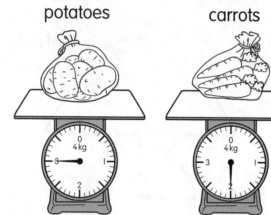 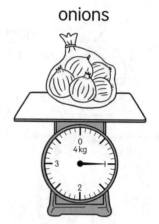

a   Which is the heaviest bag? _onions_

b   Which is the lightest bag? _carrote_

c   Arrange the bags in order of mass.
Begin with the lightest.

carrots ,   _Potatoes_ ,   _onions_
    lightest

d

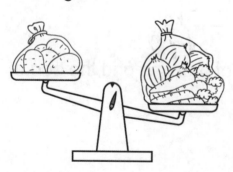

Mr.Bell puts the bags on a pan balance.
Do you think the above picture is correct? _yes_

How do you know? _because Potatoes are_
lighter than the other bag.

3 Fill in the spaces.

pumpkin
melon
pineapple

a The mass of the pumpkin is ___7___ kg.

b The mass of the melon is ___4___ kg.

c The mass of the pineapple is ___2___ kg.

d Which is the lightest? ___pineapple___

e The melon is as heavy as ___the___ pineapples.

4 Fill in the spaces.

a

Mrs Green has a mass of ___54___ kg.

b

Mr Green has a mass of ___7___ kg.

c Who is heavier, Mr Green or Mrs Green? ___Mrs green___

How much heavier? ___34___ kg

Mr Green

Mrs Green

Practice 3   Measuring in grams

1 The mass of one ☐ Ig is I g.

a

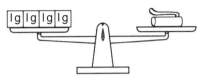

The lid of a pen has a mass of _____ g.

b

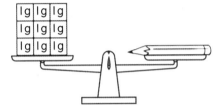

The pencil has a mass of _____ g.

c

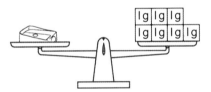

The sharpener has a mass of _____ g.

d

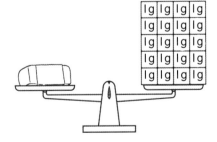

The rubber has a mass of _____ g.

2 Find the missing numbers. Fill in the boxes.

a

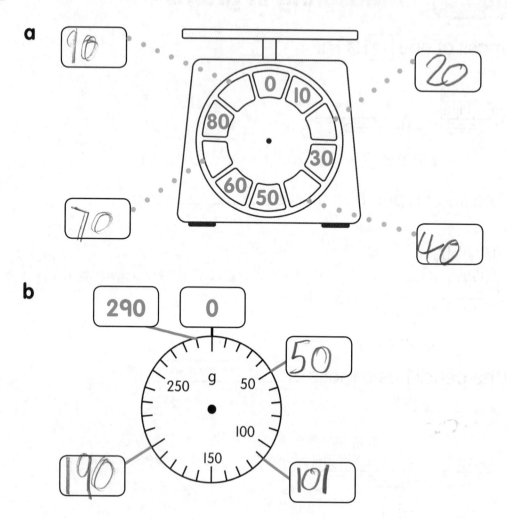

| 90 | 20 |
| 70 | 40 |

b

290   0

50

190   101

c

0   5

60

34   23

d

3 You will need fruit for this activity.
Guess the masses of the fruit and write these in the table below.
Then find the masses and complete the table.

My fruit	My guess	Actual mass
Water	2 g	1 g
Molen	g	g

Swap your fruit with a partner and repeat the activity.

Partner's fruit	My guess	Actual mass
Parga	3 g	2 g
	g	g

Do the two sets of fruit have the same
masses? _____ 06 _____

4 **What is the mass?**

a

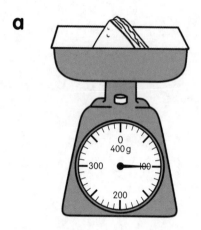

The sandwich has

a mass of ___100___ g.

b

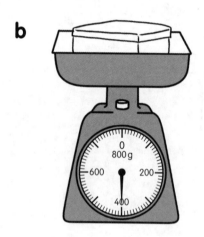

The lunch box has

a mass of ___400___ g.

c

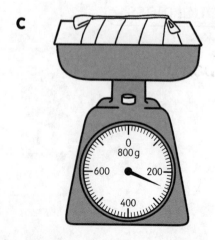

The pencil case has

a mass of ___205___ g.

d

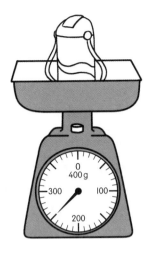

The water bottle has

a mass of ___205___ g.

e

The grapes have

a mass of ___152___ g.

f

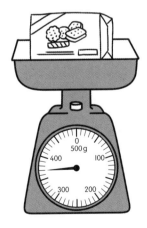

The box of biscuits has

a mass of ___352___ g.

5 Fill in the spaces.

a   The empty bowl has a mass of ___300___ g.

b   Some marbles are put into the bowl.

   The bowl and the marbles have a mass of ___502___ g

c   What is the mass of the marbles? ___500___ g

Practice 4 Comparing masses in grams

Date: _____

1 Write down the masses of these foods in the boxes.
Then fill in the spaces.

onions

200 g

pumpkin

705 g

carrots

205 g

green beans

100 g

a The ___PUMPKIN___ is the heaviest.

b The ___100___ are the lightest.

c The pumpkin is ___505___ g heavier than the onions.

d The ___POMPKIN___ are heavier than the green beans
but lighter than the carrots.

2 Look at the parcels.

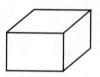

Parcel A
180 g

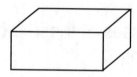

Parcel B
250 g

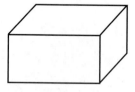

Parcel C
800 g

Parcel D
430 g

a   Which is the heaviest? ___C___

b   Which is the lightest? ___A___

c   Write **heavier** or **lighter**.

Parcel B is ___lighter___ than Parcel D.

Parcel D is ___heavier___ than Parcel A.

d   Parcel C is ___605___ g heavier than Parcel B.

e   Parcel A is ___702___ g lighter than Parcel C.

Practice 5   Addition and subtraction of mass

1 Two dogs have masses of 35 kg and 67 kg.
What is the total mass of the two dogs?

The total mass of the two dogs is __112__ kg.

2 Matt is 32 kg.
He is 5 kg lighter than Nick.
How heavy is Nick?

Nick is __37__ kg.

3 Mr Green needs 400 g of clay to make a pot.
He only has 143 g of clay.
How much more clay does he need?

He needs __343__ g more clay.

4 Emma has a mass of 25 kg.
Ahmed is 6 kg heavier than Emma.
What is their total mass?

Their total mass is ___36___ kg.

5 Mr Jones buys a bag of onions with a mass of 750 g.
He throws away 100 g of onions which are rotten.
Then he cooks 480 g.
What is the mass of onions left in the bag?

The mass of onions left in the bag is _480_ g.

6 A shopkeeper sells 45 kg of potatoes on Monday.
He sells 18 kg less potatoes on Tuesday than on Monday.
How much does he sell altogether on the two days?

He sells ___57___ kg of potatoes altogether on the two days.

Practice 6   Multiplication and division of mass

1 The mass of 5 bags of potatoes is 30 kg.
Each bag has the same mass.
What is the mass of each bag?

The mass of each bag is ___6___ kg.

2 There are 6 bricks.
Each brick has a mass of 3 kg.
What is the total mass of the 6 bricks?

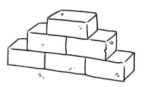

The total mass of the 6 bricks is ___18___ kg.

3 A sharpener has a mass of 10 g.
What is the total mass of 7 sharpeners?

The total mass of 7 sharpeners is ___70___ g.

4 The total mass of 3 packets of pasta is 6 kg.
Each packet has the same mass.
What is the mass of each packet of pasta?

The mass of each packet of pasta is ___2___ kg.

5 The total mass of some cherries is 36 g.
Each cherry has a mass of 4 g.
How many cherries are there?

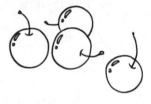

There are ___9___ cherries.

6 There are 4 bags of rice.
Each bag has a mass of 8 kg.
What is the total mass of the 4 bags of rice?

The total mass of the 4 bags of rice is ___32___ kg.

Challenging Practice

1 Draw the needle on Scale B. Show where it should point to.

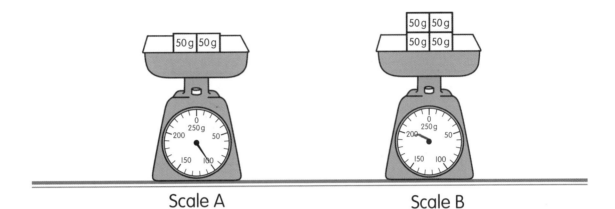

Scale A   Scale B

2 There are 3 [100 g] on Scale A.

How many [100 g] must there be on Scale B?

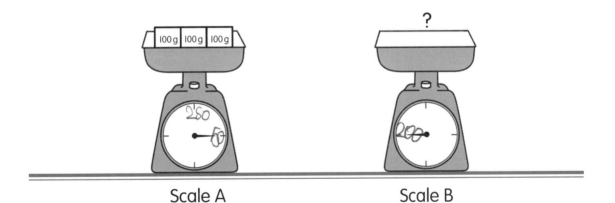

Scale A   Scale B

_200_ [100 g] are on Scale B.

3

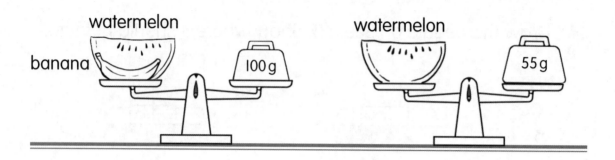

The banana has a mass of ___50___ g.

4

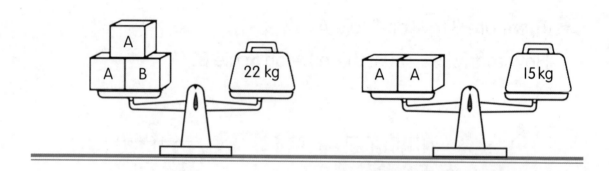

Box B has a mass of ___4___ kg.

Revision 1

Revision 1

Date: _____

Section A
Choose the correct answer.
Write its letter in the box.

1 Which one of the following shows three hundred and four?

    a   34   **b**   304

    c   340   **d**   344

2 What is the number shown in the chart?

Hundreds	Tens	Ones
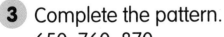		

    a   450   **b**   405

    c   350   **d**   315

3 Complete the pattern.

    650, 760, 870, _____

    a   890   **b**   950

    c   980   **d**   1000

4 Add the two numbers shown on the chart.

Hundreds	Tens	Ones

   a   879   **b**   560

   c   319   **d**   241

b

5 $275 + 14 =$ _560_

   a   279   **b**   289

   c   379   **d**   415

415

6 Add 536 and 287.

   a   913   **b**   823

   c   723   **d**   249

723

7 Subtract the two numbers shown on the chart.

Hundreds	Tens	Ones

   a   488   **b**   367

   c   246   **d**   121

a

8 Subtract.

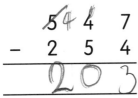

a 801 b 393
c 313 d 293

9 Look at the three digits.

2   7   5

Use the digits to make the greatest and smallest 3-digit numbers.
What is the answer when you subtract the numbers?

a 587 b 505
c 495 d 477

10 Jack has 86 marbles.
Farha has 74 marbles.
How many marbles do they have altogether?

a 12 b 86
c 150 d 160

11 Mr James has £125.
He uses £70 to buy a pair of shoes.
How much does he have left?

a £195 b £87
c £75 d £55

12 Look at the picture.

How many flowers are there?

a   2 × 7   b   7 × 5 ✓

c   6 × 6   d   7 × 6

13 Look at the dot paper.
Which multiplication sentence does it show?

a   3 × 3   b   3 × 4

c   4 × 4   d   12 × 4

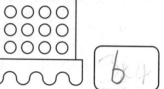

14 Multiply 2 by 3. What is the answer?

a   1   b   5

c   6   d   0

15 A shopkeeper has 10 boxes of oranges.
Each box contains 3 oranges.
How many oranges does the shopkeeper have altogether?

a   7   b   10

c   13   d   30 ✓

16 Miya has 4 boxes and 32 badges.
She puts an equal number of badges into each of the boxes.
How many badges are there in each box?

a   36   b   28

c   ⑧   d   4 ✓

17 The length of a biscuit tin is about __1cm__.

a   25 cm   b   25 m

c   1 cm   d   1 m

18 Omar has a ribbon 100 cm long.
He uses 45 cm of it to wrap a present.
What is the length of ribbon left?

a   155 cm

b   100 cm

c   55 cm

d   65 cm ✓

d

19 A bottle of juice has a mass of 450 g.
A shopkeeper puts it into a box with a mass of 37 g.
What is the total mass of the bottle and the box?

a   413 g

b   417 g

c   (487 g)

d   820 g

C

20 Ruby buys 35 marbles on Monday.
She buys 21 marbles on Tuesday.
She gives away 40 of these marbles.
How many marbles does she have left?

a   14

b   16 ✓

c   56

d   96

b

Section B
Read the questions and fill in the answers.

21 Write 386 in words.

three hundred and eighty six

22 Arrange the following in order, beginning with the greatest.

609   712   699   543

712 , 699 , 609 , 643
greatest

23 Add 46 and 63.   _109_

24 Add 507 and 52.   _559_

25 Do the sum.

$$
\begin{array}{r}
4\ \ 3\ \ 8 \\
+\ \ 1\ \ 5\ \ 6 \\
\hline
5\ \ 9\ \ 4 \\
\hline
\end{array}
$$
                                         _594_

26 A shopkeeper has £746.
She gets another £198.
How much does she have altogether?   £ _814_

27 Subtract 17 from 831.   _766_

28 Team A scores 270 points.
Team B scores 363 points.
How many more points does Team B score
than Team A?   _110_

29 Subtract 284 from 861.   _125_

30 There are 200 beads.
94 of the beads are red.
The rest are yellow.
How many yellow beads are there?
Complete the model and find the answer.

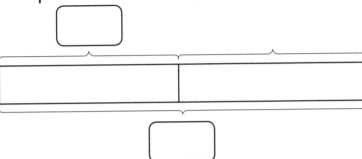

100

31 There are 138 cars and 27 vans in a car park.
How many vehicles are there altogether?
Draw a model and find the answer.

358

32 Draw ☆ to show 5 groups of 3.
Then fill in the spaces.

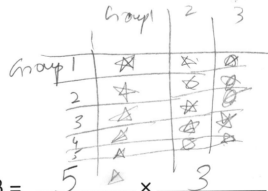

5 groups of 3 = _____*5*_____ × _____*3*_____

= _____*15*_____

33 Draw a model to show 2 groups of 10.

34 What is 7 × 4?   _28_

35 Fill in the spaces.

8 × 4 = _32_   4 × 8 = _32_   _32_ ÷ 4 = 8

36 Peter has 24 grapes.
He gives 8 grapes to each of his friends.
He has none left.
How many friends are there?   _16_

37 What is the length of this line?

_____   _9_ cm

38 Tai makes a square using 24 cm of string.
The 4 sides are equal.
What is the length of each side of the square?

 ?

_____6_____ cm

39 The mass of a bottle of water is 2 kg.
What is the mass of 9 bottles of water?

_____18_____ kg

40 What is the mass of the cherries?

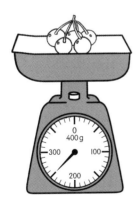

_____205_____ g

Section C
Read the questions.
Show your workings in the spaces provided.

41 Miss Brook has £245.
She uses £98 to buy a radio.
How much does Miss Brook have left?

43

£ _43_

42 Tai puts 8 toy cars into each box.
How many toy cars are there in 6 boxes?

8 × 6 =

_46_ toy cars

43 Anna has £352.
Ravi has £168 more than she has.
   a   How much does Ravi have?
   b   How much do both of them have altogether?

     a £ 520

     b £ 419

44 Hardeep makes 120 jam tarts on Saturday and another
93 jam tarts on Sunday.
   a   How many jam tarts does Hardeep make altogether?
   b   If Hardeep sells 207 jam tarts, how many jam tarts will
he have left?

     a 213 jam tarts

     b 106 jam tarts

45 Miya has 249 cards.
Jack has 53 fewer cards than Miya.
Ella has 79 more cards than Jack.
How many cards does Ella have?

_____275_____ cards